Coloring Books
Butterfly Swirls

ISBN: 978-1-940282-88-6

Grab your coloring pencils or crayons.
Sit back. And have fun!

You will love this beautiful coloring book.
It's simply gorgeous!

Beautiful Butterflies
Flowing Images
A Relaxing Good Time

Inside you will find swirling images of beautiful flowers and butterflies.

Each coloring page is located on the right side of the coloring book; the left side is blank, leaving it free for you to create beautiful drawings of your own, journal your thoughts, or simply leave as is.

Sample Images...

Made in the USA
Lexington, KY
18 November 2016